INTRODUCTION

Burton Glen
Charter Academy
4171 E Atherton Rd
Burton, MI 48519

Mimi's Book of Colors will assist toddlers with recognizing twelve colors through various fun coloring activities. Learning these twelve colors by doing engaging coloring activities is also a great way to enhance your toddlers fine motor skills. So come on grab your crayons and learn colors with Mimi!!

This Book Belongs To

Yellow Color

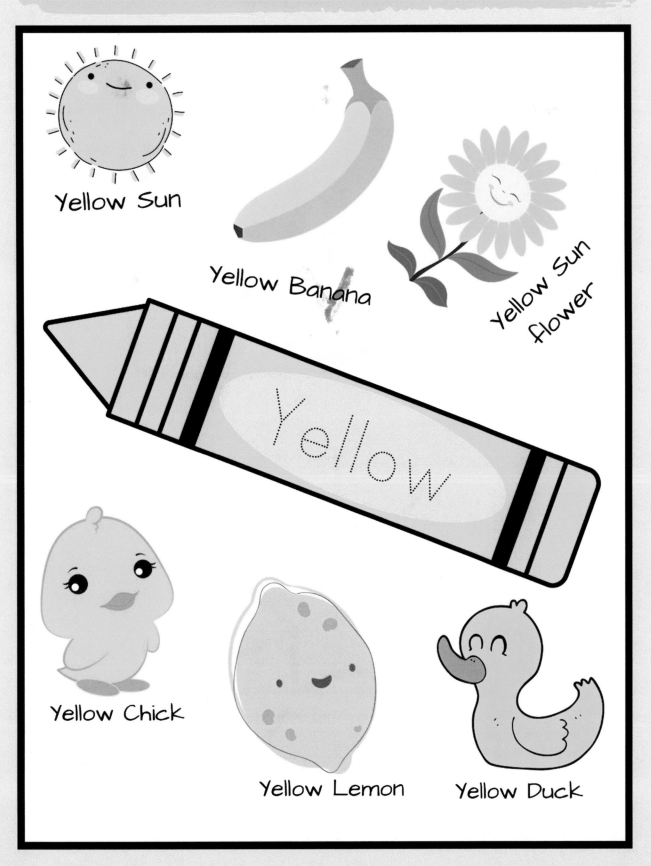

Yellow Sun

Yellow Banana

Yellow Sun flower

Yellow

Yellow Chick

Yellow Lemon

Yellow Duck

Coloring Activity

Use yellow crayon to fill in.

Blue Color

Blue Whale

Blue Car

Blue Bird

Blue

Blue Sky

Blue Book

Blue Shoes

Coloring Activity

Use blue crayon to fill in.

Red Color

Red Apple

Red Lipstick

Red Rooster

Red

Red Strawberry

Red Heart

Red Cupcake

Coloring Activity

Use red crayon to fill in.

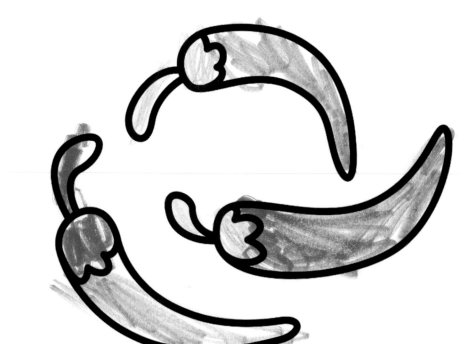

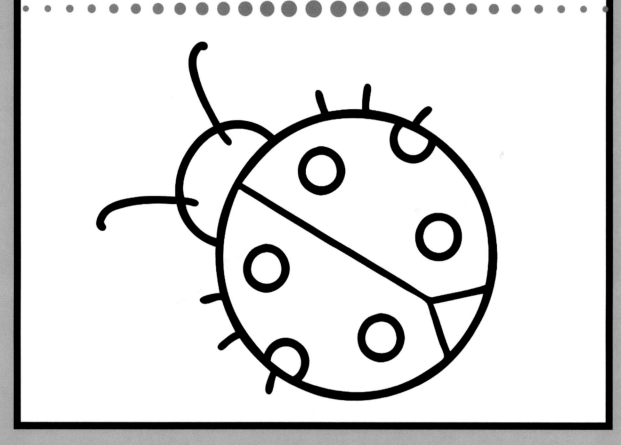

Pink Color

Pink Bunny

Pink Flower

Pink Flamingo

Pink

Pink Donut

Pink Telephone

Pink Glasses

Coloring Activity

Use pink crayon to fill in.

Green Color

Green Plant

Green Turtle

Green Trex

Green

Green Rocket

Green Apple

Green Peas

Coloring Activity

Use green crayon to fill in.

Orange Color

Orange
Orange

Orange
Pumpkin

Orange
Parrot

Orange

Orange
Basketball

Orange
Leaves

Orange Tiger

Coloring Activity

Use orange crayon to fill in.

Purple Color

Purple Sweater

Purple flower

Purple Candle

Purple

Purple Grapes

Purple Purse

Purple Candy

Coloring Activity

Use purple crayon to fill in.

Brown Color

Brown Hat

Brown Leaf

Brown Bear

Brown

Brown Beans

Brown Jacket

Brown Sparrow

Coloring Activity

Use brown crayon to fill in.

Gray Color

Gray Ghost

Gray Fish

Gray Airplane

Gray

Gray Elephant

Gray Feather

Gray Clouds

Coloring Activity

Use gray crayon to fill in.

Magenta Color

Magenta Cupcake

Magenta Leaves

Magenta Mermaid

Magenta

Magenta Glass

Magenta Skooter

Magenta Bubble

Coloring Activity

Use magenta crayon to fill in.

White Color

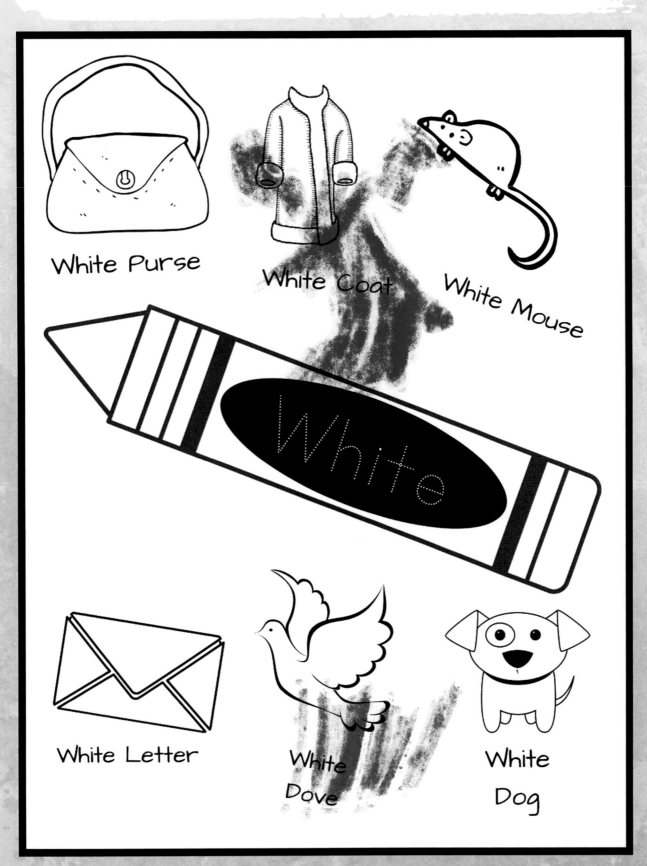

White Purse

White Coat

White Mouse

White

White Letter

White Dove

White Dog

Coloring Activity

Use any crayon to fill in.

Black Color

Black Umbrella

Black Tire

Black Shoes

Black

Black Car

Black Wallet

Black Camera

Coloring Activity

Use black crayon to fill in.

 red

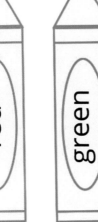 green

 blue

 yellow

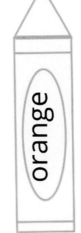 orange

 pink

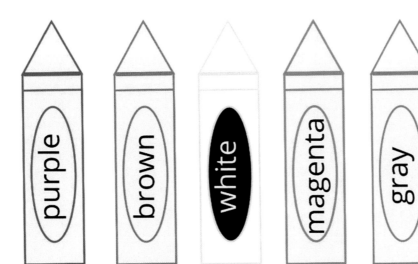 purple brown white magenta gray Black

Cut and Paste activity

Cut colored crayons and paste over correct empty crayons.

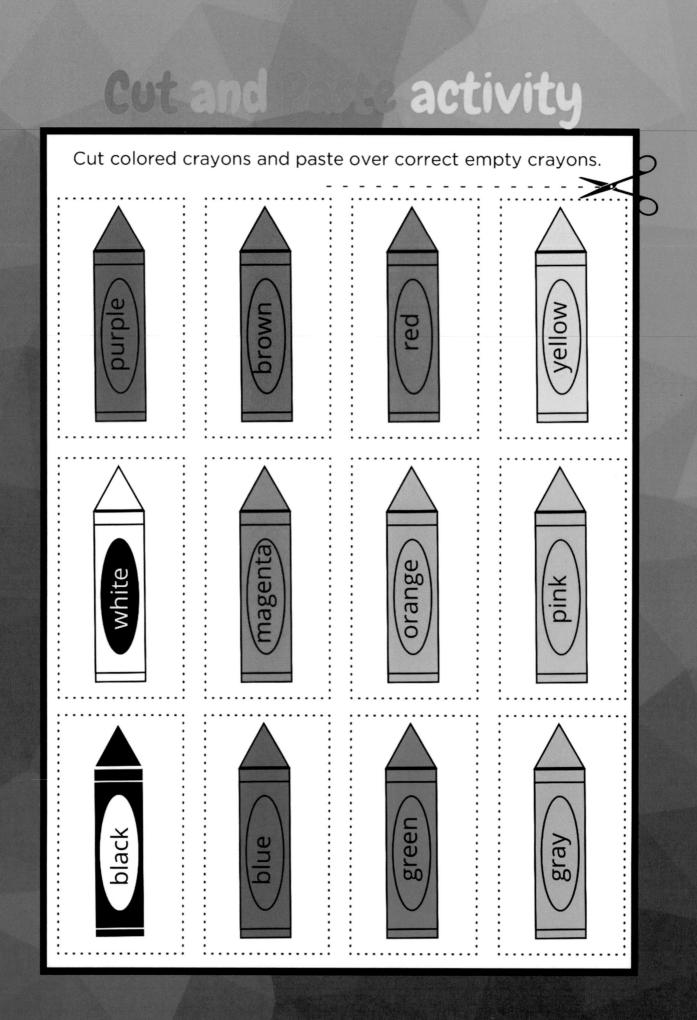